LIFE
and
LOVE

LGBTQ+ Adult Coloring Book

Inspiring Messages
and Meditations

by
Ronald Holt and
William Huggett

People within the LGBTQ+ communities face unique challenges every day.

LIFE and LOVE: LGBTQ+ Adult Coloring Book provides a path toward hope through coloring and reflection. There are 39 designs for coloring. Each has an affirmation, inspiring quote and a message for meditation. The book is designed to help you find strength and encouragement in these challenging times.

Each person has their own journey and must forge a healing path. But we celebrate a deeper shared strength. Our greatest strength comes from diversity.

We are all different. We come in many different shapes and designs. Each one of us is a unique design.

Every person needs to connect with their authentic self and bring it into the light. This will help the world move forward. Embracing diversity makes us stronger.

LIFE and LOVE: LGBTQ+ Adult Coloring Book celebrates this wonderful tapestry.

Always remember; you are worthy of unconditional love and acceptance – just the way you are.

To get more information about Dr. Holt, his speaking engagements, other books or videos, please visit DrRonHolt.com. You can find more information about Dr. Huggett at WilliamHuggett.com.

Sincerely-

"Hide not your talents, they for use were made.
What's a sundial in the shade?"
—Benjamin Franklin

You're here for a reason.

Your authentic self is the greatest gift you have for the world.

So today, sit with full awareness of this
precious gift that is you.

Know you are worthy of love.

Affirmation: I am standing firm in love,
starting today and every day.

"To thine own self be true."
—Shakespeare

Your life is a beautiful gift.

It is a gift that comes with profound responsibility.
It's up to you to define and live your life.

As part of your meditation today,
observe the color you bring to the design.

Remember to bring color and beauty to the design that is
you.

Live your life without fear of what others think of you.

Affirmation: Today I will move toward
a higher version of my authentic self.

"There is only one journey.
Going inside yourself."
—Rainer Maria Rilke

Today as you meditate on the mandala,
notice that each piece contributes to the whole.

No single piece is more important than the next.
Each part is necessary for the wholeness of the design.

Next, see yourself in the design,
recognize the many features and aspects of yourself.

All these parts come together in the beautiful,
intricate design that is you.

Affirmation: Today, I welcome the journey into myself.

"Love grows by giving.
The love we give away is the only love we keep.
The only way to retain love is to give it away."
—Elbert Hubbard

You contain one of the most precious resources on earth...
love.

It has the power to heal.
Love transcends all limits.

Love will always triumph over fear and hate.

The more love you give away,
the more it springs up inside of you.

So today, bask in this abundant and valuable
resource that wells up within you.

Affirmation: I give love away freely and indiscriminately.

**"*Yesterday is but today's memory,*
and tomorrow is today's dream."
*—Khalil Gibran***

There is no wrong time for love.
There is only the present moment.

As you meditate today, first,
allow yourself to know you are worthy of love.

Next, take a few moments and think about who loves you.
Picture the person or animal in your mind.

Then, with this awareness, let love flow outward.
Let it land on whoever you meet today.

And remember to check-in with yourself often.
Extend love to yourself as you go through each day.

Affirmation: I honor myself by connecting
to the present moment.

"It's not the mountain we conquer, but ourselves."
— Sir Edmund Hillary

Meditation Exercise.

Move in real close to the mandala.
Select one small segment of a line.
Focus your attention on that one
tiny portion for a few moments.

This single piece represents the present moment
and who you are right now.

Then, allow your visual field to move outward and notice how
the lines come together to form small parts of the mandala.

Then, observe how these small segments
come together to create the overall design.

Sometimes it's hard to make sense of where
the present moment fits in with your overall life.

So you may need to take a step back and recognize
the present moment is part of a larger design.

Affirmation: I recognize my current situation
is part of a larger picture.

"Seize the moments of happiness, love and be loved!
That is the only reality in the world, all else is folly."
—Leo Tolstoy

The moments of life form a continuous flow.
Each moment comes and goes.
Once it's over, it is forever released from the present.

There are no do-overs.

So grab hold of each moment.

Stay grounded and aware.

Connect with the present moment.
Observe how love is all around and within you.

cherish all of the little moments

grounded in LOVE

Affirmation: I am present for myself and those I love.

"It's the action, not the fruit of the action, that's important. You have to do the right thing. It may not be in your power, may not be in your time, that there'll be any fruit. But that doesn't mean you stop doing the right thing. You may never know what results come from your action.
But if you do nothing, there will be no result."
—Mahatma Gandhi

Giving love is like tossing a pebble into a pond of water.
The effect continues way beyond the initial act.
You have no control over the ripples.

Likewise, an act of love creates a change in the world.
The effect spreads out in all directions.

Start today, and create some
ripples in the universe with your love.

Then allow yourself to be free once you've released them.

Affirmation: Today I will create some ripples in the universe.

"Love all, trust a few, do wrong to none."
— William Shakespeare

Love is a reliable guide.
It will lead you to a higher version of yourself.

Start each day by grounding yourself in love.
Spend a few moments sitting with an awareness of
something or someone you love.

Connect with this feeling.

Then take the next step.

Recognize that this external person or thing
is merely a vehicle that helps you to connect with love.

Love is always there.
It's always around you and within you.

Affirmation: Love is my trusted companion.

"Let the beauty of what you love, be what you do."
— Rumi

As you color the mandala, notice how a vibrant image emerges from a simple pattern of black lines on white paper.

You are transforming the mandala by
bringing color to the design.

Your creation is unique.

Likewise, you are a unique design.
And you are beautiful.

So create your beautiful and unique self
and let it be visible to the world.

This is your gift to yourself and the world.

Affirmation: I'm giving the world my authentic self.

*"I wake at dawn with a winged heart
and give thanks for another day of loving."
—Kahlil Gibran*

Allow yourself to sit in silence for a few moments.

Become aware of your breathing.
Notice the cycle of breathing.
There is inhalation followed by exhalation.
It is a continuous flow.

Some people focus on breathing
to anchor them while they meditate.

Love is like breathing.
It is a consistent anchor.
It cycles. You take it in and give it away.

You can't control where the air goes after you exhale.
Likewise, as you release love into the world, let it go.

This cycle allows space for more love to enter your life.

Affirmation: Breathing reminds me of
the continuous flow of love in my life.

"Where there is great love there are always miracles."
—Willa Cather

Love transforms everything it encounters.

When fear and hatred become surrounded by love,
they give way to peace and healing.

Love is a miracle.

So experience this miracle within you.

Affirmation: Today I am experiencing the miracle of love.

"Love is space and time measured by the heart."
— Marcel Proust

The universe is expanding.
And knowledge of the universe is expanding.

Your capacity for love is like the universe.

It continues to expand.

There is no limit to love.

There is an endless current of love all around and within you.

Allow yourself to be gently carried along this current.

Affirmation: Today I open my mind and flow with love.

*"The key to growth is the introduction
of higher dimensions of consciousness
into our awareness."*
—Lao Tzu

Human consciousness is evolving.

We understand gender
is much more than a simple binary concept.

This understanding is leading us to
a deeper appreciation of what it means to be human.

Remember that labels only go so far.
They are the evolving attempts with
language to grasp complex human realities.

So don't be constrained by labels.

Your gender identity is unique to you.

Live the life that is most authentic to you.

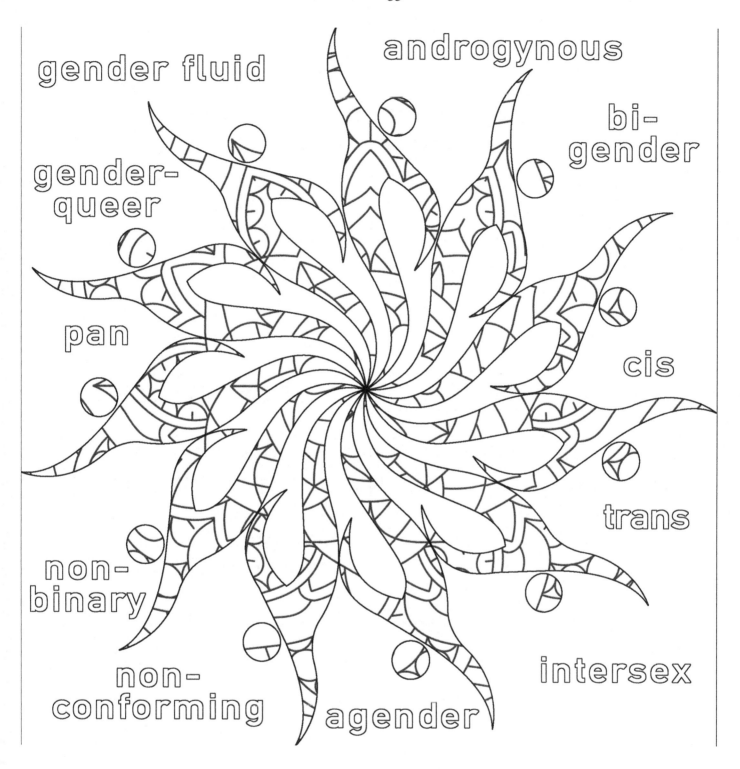

gender fluid

androgynous

bi-gender

genderqueer

pan

cis

non-binary

trans

non-conforming

agender

intersex

Affirmation: I will lead human consciousness
by being the most authentic version of myself.

"A loving heart is the truest wisdom."
—Charles Dickens

There may be times when you feel confused or lost.

Do not be afraid of these moments.
These experiences can guide you to profound growth.

When you feel confused,
be still and connect with the love deep within you.

Then let love guide you.

Affirmation: Love guides me.

"We love the things we love for what they are."
— Robert Frost

Everyone is worthy of love.

The simple words "I love you"
can be communicated in many ways.

Some of the most powerful messages of love are your actions.

So today, DO something loving for yourself.

Then do something loving for someone you care about.

And finally, find an opportunity today to
do something loving for a complete stranger.

Affirmation: We are all connected through love.

"Grief can be the garden of compassion.
If you keep your heart open through everything,
your pain can become your greatest ally in
your life's search for love and wisdom."
— Rumi

Sometimes you may feel alone,
and you may believe no one loves you.

These feeling are often rooted in fear,
and they are false.

So don't be misled.

Whenever they pop up, allow them to pass.

And let yourself stay grounded in hope.

Allow love and hope to be your trusted travel companions.

Affirmation: I invite love and wisdom into my life.

"All that we love deeply becomes part of us."
—Helen Keller

Each day we must stand strong.
Sometimes we may be overcome with fear.

But remember, you have a greater strength within you.

Love is the greatest source of strength.
It is a fire that burns brighter than fear.

Love is your most true essence.
It is in every part of your being.

So today, commit to unleash this powerful force.

Stand strong, stay grounded in love.

Affirmation: I welcome love that is authentic and real.

**_"What lies behind us and what lies before us
are tiny matters compared to what lies within us."
— Oliver Wendell Holmes_**

Other people cannot dictate who you are
or who you love.

Your love is the most precious gift you have.

So cherish your capacity to love.

And hold those you love with gentle care.

Affirmation: I honor and cherish love in my life.

"You must be the change you wish to see in the world."
— Mahatma Gandhi

You are a magnificent force for change.
But this change starts with loving and accepting yourself.

Use the mandala as a tool to embrace
yourself with love and acceptance.

Start by looking at the mandala and the many
little pieces that come together in the design.

Then, take a moment to reflect on the many parts of yourself.

Let each segment of the mandala represent a part of yourself.

As you color each part of the mandala,
embrace each new piece of yourself.

Soon you will have created a beautiful you.
And this is the change the world needs most.

Affirmation: I am beautiful. I embrace change. I am love.

"However mean your life is,
meet it and live it;
do not shun it and call it hard names."
—Henry David Thoreau

Life is not always comfortable.

Sometimes it can appear the world doesn't support you,
but don't give up hope.

When the winds of life blow against you,
allow love to be the wings that lift you.

Affirmation: I use adversity to grow.

"Your days are numbered. Use them to throw open the windows of your soul to the sun."
—Marcus Aurelius

One of the greatest gifts of the human mind is the ability to understand mortality.

Mortality is the backdrop for life.
It gives meaning to life.

Cherish each moment of life.
You will never experience this moment again.

Life is beautiful and so are you.

Live life fully and love unconditionally.

Affirmation: I seize each moment of my life.

*"What we have done for ourselves alone
dies with us.
What we have done for others and the world
remains and is immortal."
—Albert Pike*

We are all mortal beings,
but our actions reverberate far beyond
the limits of our lives.

Each moment of life is priceless.
And every moment gives you an opportunity
to create something new.

Affirmation: I stand firm fully alive and grounded by love.

"Sadness is but a wall between two gardens."
—Kahlil Gibran

There will be times when your heart gets broken.
There will be times when you lose someone you love.
There will be times when you do not feel love.

These moments contain hidden treasures.

Even though you may not feel it now,
these experiences will one day wrap you in wisdom.

So don't quit.
Don't let your heart shrink or hesitate.
Find life and love in the present moment.
Live and love.

Affirmation: My heart will heal.

"Who can give law to lovers?
Love is unto itself a higher law."
—Boethius

Today observe the transformation that occurs
as you add color to the mandala.

Love is the color of life.
It transforms a world of black and white.

Each day, select at least one small segment of your life
and add love to it.

Do this every day.

Soon you will have created a beautiful design.

Affirmation: Today I am adding love to my life.

"Let yourself be silently drawn
by the strange pull of what you really love.
It will not lead you astray."
— Rumi

Your most profound truth
can reveal itself through feelings and emotions.

Sometimes this can be frightening.
But don't give in to fear.

Love is an excellent guide to what is real and true.

So today, be open as love reveals truth and beauty to you.

Take time today to sit in silence.
Listen to the stillness within.

Affirmation: I will listen to silence and hear the universe.

*"The beginning of love is the will to let those we love
be perfectly themselves,
the resolution not to twist them to fit our own image.
If in loving them we do not love what they are,
but only their potential likeness to ourselves,
then we do not love them:
we only love the reflection
of ourselves we find in them."
—Thomas Merton*

Love is a powerful instrument when it's given away.
But sometimes we love others with conditions
or because we seek love in return.

Today's goal is to give love to someone
with no expectations in return.

Do something loving for another.

Remember the other person is free to respond
any way they chose.
They may not react the way you expect,
or they may not respond at all.

The goal is to give your love away.

Affirmation: I am becoming a philanthropist of love.

"The consciousness of loving and being loved brings a warmth and richness to life that nothing else can bring."
—Oscar Wilde

Life has many vibrant and beautiful textures.

Families come in many shapes and sizes.

What defines a family is love.

Love is both the canvas and the paint of a family.
It is the background and foreground of relationships.

Take time today to notice the different ways
love is always present within and around you.

Affirmation: I am fully alive, and life supports me.
I have family in those I love.

"Knowing yourself is the beginning of all wisdom."
— Aristotle

You are complex.
It takes a lifetime of learning to understand oneself.
Sometimes other people can show you
unknown parts of yourself.

Some of these best teachers
are the people you have strong reactions toward.

If you have strong reactions to someone,
take a moment to reflect.

Start by sitting with an open mind.

Then see if you can notice ways you might embody the same
traits you're reacting to in the other person.

Once you can tolerate this awareness,
allow yourself to embrace yourself.

Embrace every part of yourself in healing love.

Affirmation: I am getting to know and accept myself.

"Being deeply loved by someone gives you strength,
while loving someone deeply gives you courage."
— Lao Tzu

Love is a powerful key that unlocks the human potential.

Unconditional love guides us to the highest levels
of what it means to be human.

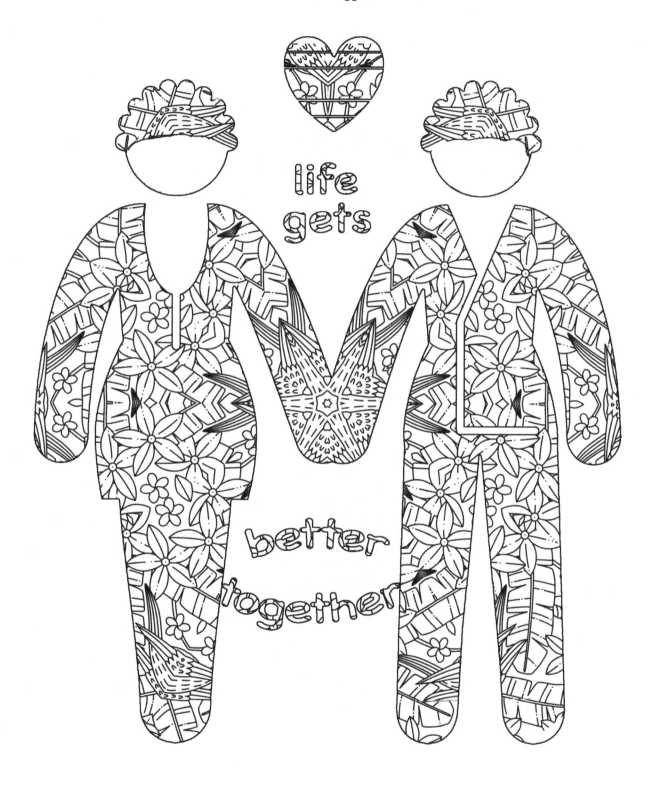

Affirmation: Today I embrace the courage to love and the courage that comes from loving.

"The power of imagination makes us infinite."
— John Muir

Human beings are able to
give love,
receive love
and observe love
all at the same time.

Today as you color the mandala,
reflect on the ways you are
the conscious manifestation of love.

Embrace your ability to be conscious of love.

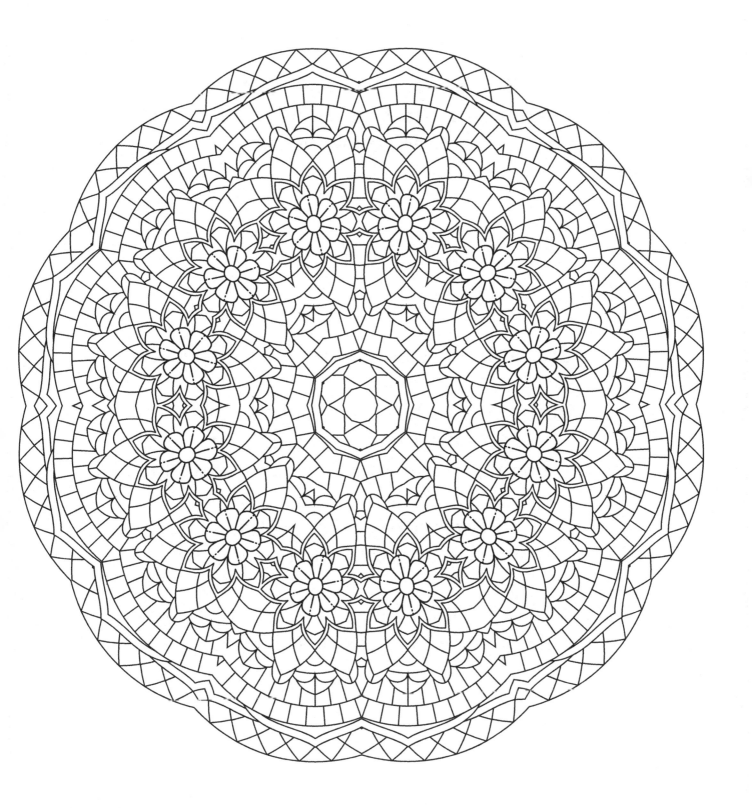

Affirmation: My capacity to love
is greater than I can imagine.

*"The future belongs to those
who believe in the beauty of their dreams."
— Eleanor Roosevelt*

A dream lives deep inside of every person.

You may not be aware of your dream.
But when you get close to it,
you recognize it because it feels real and true.

These dreams are gifts.
They guide and inform your journey.

Expand and allow yourself to live this dream.
Let your life align with these desires deep within you.

Affirmation: I allow myself to dream.

"The weak can never forgive.
Forgiveness is the attribute of the strong."
—Mahatma Gandhi

Forgiveness is an act of stepping away from
the pain of your injury.

When you forgive someone else,
you release yourself from holding onto the pain.
The other person's actions are no longer
in control of your healing.

You create greater space for yourself.

Even now, as you sit with pain,
recognize a new space is patiently waiting for you.

So today, if you feel hurt, allow yourself to be free.
You deserve to have peace.

Release yourself.

Affirmation: Today I harness the strength
and healing power of forgiveness.

"The best way to find yourself is to lose
yourself in the service of others."
— Mahatma Gandhi

Service is one way to nurture yourself.

When you give to another in service,
you will uncover valuable information about yourself.

Affirmation: Today I will learn something new
about myself by being of service to others.

*"Love is the only force capable of transforming
an enemy into a friend."
— MLK Jr.*

Love helps us see the frightened,
vulnerable child that is deep within those we fear.

Love gives us the strength to release pain thru forgiveness.

Love leads us toward understanding and compassion.

Affirmation: Love will transform me,
my community, and the world.

"Perhaps all the dragons in our lives are princesses
who are only waiting to see us act, just once,
with beauty and courage.
Perhaps everything that frightens us is,
in its deepest essence,
something helpless that wants our love."
— Rainer Maria Rilke

Notice whenever fear,
hatred or prejudice show up in your life.
Sometimes you'll experience them in others, and sometimes
you'll find them inside yourself.

These feelings might reveal that a person
has become disconnected from love.

So whenever you notice these feelings,
just acknowledge them.

Then, with compassion, allow these feelings to
sit down at the table in the company of love.

Over time fear, hatred and prejudice will fade.

Affirmation: Love is greater than fear, hatred, and prejudice.

*"There are only two ways to live your life.
One as though nothing is a miracle.
The other is as though everything is a miracle."
—Albert Einstein*

A miracle can be defined as something that is
highly improbable or extraordinary.

Of the 7.5 billion human beings alive today or
the over 100 billion that have ever lived,
you are unique.

There has never been another you.
It's pretty clear you are a miracle.

For today's meditation, notice how you are unique.
Then reflect on the miracle of you.

Circle yourself with love and acceptance of this miracle.
Then, recognize all the other miracles in your life.
Extend your love and acceptance to these miracles.

Soon you will be aware of many miracles in your life.

Affirmation: I am a unique and special individual.

"Is the oak better than the acorn
which is its fullness and completion?"
—Ralph Waldo Emerson

You are a work in progress.
Do not expect perfection,
but be present with each step along your journey.

Some periods will be challenging.
There may be times you feel like giving up.

But always remember, deep within you,
there is a seed that is your future self.

Nurture yourself today and every day.

With time, this tiny seed will grow into the mighty oak tree.

Affirmation: I accept and embrace
myself as a work in progress.

"Nobody cares how much you know until
they know how much you care."
—Theodore Roosevelt

We are all connected.

It's clear that loving others is a gift to them.
But it is also true that loving
and accepting yourself, creates healing.

Loving others and yourself are two
of the most powerful tools at your disposal.

Love is how you offer your most beautiful gift to the world.

Affirmation: I celebrate my connection to all of life.

Made in the USA
Coppell, TX
21 June 2020